# Solo
by
# Choice

## SECOND EDITION

# CAREER RESOURCES for a LIFE in the LAW

### FROM LAWYERAVENUE PRESS

## The New What Can You Do With a Law Degree?
*A Lawyer's Guide to Career Satisfaction Inside, Outside & Around the Law*
By Larry Richard & Tanya Hanson  •  $30 / 220 pages (2012)

### The New Lawyer Survival Guide, Vol. 1:
## From Lemons to Lemonade in the New Legal Job Market
*Winning Job Search Strategies for Entry-Level Attorneys*
By Richard L. Hermann  •  $30 / 254 pages (2012)

### The New Lawyer Survival Guide, Vol. 2:
## Small Firms, Big Opportunity
*How to Get Hired (and Succeed) in the New Legal Economy*
By Linda Calvert Hanson, Samantha Williams  •  $30 /168 pages (2012)

### The New Lawyer Survival Guide, Vol. 3:
## Becoming a Rural Lawyer
*A Personal Guide to Establishing a Small Town Practice*
By Bruce M. Cameron  •  $30 / 148 pages (2013)

## Solo by Choice Second Edition
*How to Be the Lawyer You Always Wanted to Be*
By Carolyn Elefant  •  $45 / 306 pages (2nd Ed., 2011)

## Solo by Choice, The Companion Guide
*34 Questions That Could Transform Your Legal Career*
By Carolyn Elefant  •  $30 / 136 pages (2011)

## Should You Really Be a Lawyer?
*The Guide to Smart Career Choices Before, During & After Law School*
By Deborah Schneider & Gary Belsky  •  $25 / 276 pages (2nd Ed., 2013)

## How to Litigate
*The Crash Course for Trial Counsel*
By Martin L. Grayson  •  $30 / 170 pages (2013)

# Solo
## by •
# Choice

## SECOND EDITION

---

### How to Be the Lawyer
### You Always Wanted to Be

**CAROLYN ELEFANT**

**DB DecisionBooks**
Seattle, Washington

Published by LawyerAvenue Press, a division of Avenue Productions, Inc.

Cover and interior design by Rose Michelle Taverniti

Solo by Choice / Second Edition is a print-on-demand re-issue originally published in October, 2011. Volume discounts available from LawyerAvenue Press. Email to editor@LawyerAvenue.com, or write to Avenue Productions, 4701 SW Admiral Way #116, Seattle WA 98116

Author Carolyn Elefant is a frequent presenter at bar conferences and law firm events on social and small firm practice trends, the ethics of social media, the nuts and bolts of 21st Century solo practice and the future of law. For more information, contact the author at www.MyShingle.com

Library of Congress Cataloging-in-Publication Data

Elefant, Carolyn.
  Solo by choice second edition : how to be the lawyer you always wanted to be / Carolyn Elefant. -- 2nd ed.
      p. cm.
   ISBN 978-0-940675-83-4 (alk. paper)
  1.  Solo law practice--United States. 2.  Practice of law--United States. 3  Law offices--United States. 4.  Lawyers--United States.  I. Title.
   KF300.E42 2011
   340.023'73--dc22
                                        2011013883

at up-tempo songs only, but not too vigorously like I've had no home training, no syncopation with the claps—leave that to the elders. No staring at anyone, even the spirit-filled or pitiable. And these are the easy rules, the ones for the very young. *No problem. No problem,* I say with nods. And if you are very good, do it all to your utmost like Noah, just so, you, too, will be rewarded with belief. Oh, Phyllis, to believe anyway. What are you made of? I start my house-to-house record:

*Dear Philip Larkin: I have felt your breath on my heart today. Phyllis said she likes to keep an open mind and I fear this is the beginning. I will not go down the long slide with you, but stay safe, a dirtroader myself. It is safe here. The copse of pines, poplars and weeds years too far gone for bush hogging choke out everything but light. Don't you see that? If you can't, I can't love you. Doesn't scripture say to stay away from bad associates? Friends who will see you dead, all in the name of opening your mind? What about knowing every single thing for sure? What about that?*

"A good day. Really good day," Leslie says. "How did you like your first visit to the territory? Different, huh?"

I nod.

"You seem preoccupied. Are you thinking about a certain young man?" Leslie starts the engine, grins at my shock that she takes for proof of her suspicion. My body shudders at the thought. I would see Bobby at the Kingdom Hall when Leslie drops me off. I'll see him the next morning at the Sunday service and the day after that on the bus. But the thought of his thick fingers anyplace on my body, his short-sleeved dress shirts with the sweaty armpits stains that never seemed to